D0120764

Kipper was sad because the magic key would not glow. He looked at the key for a long time. At last he fell asleep. Suddenly, the key glowed and the magic began to work.

Kipper's toys were coming to life. Teddy gave
Kipper a shake.

"Wake up," he said. "The magic key is
glowing. The magic is working."

Kipper sat up and rubbed his eyes. He looked at his toys.

"Come on, Kipper," said Catsimir. "Hurry up! It's time for a magic adventure."

The toys ran to the little house.

"Hurry up, Kipper," called Teddy. "Be quick,
or it will be too late."

Kipper could feel the magic working. It pulled
him inside the magic house.

The magic whizzed Kipper round and round.
"Oh help," called Kipper. "I feel different.
This is a different sort of magic."

The magic took them to an airport. It was a very busy airport. Catsimir was excited.

"Maybe we can catch a plane," he said.

"Maybe we can have an exciting adventure!"

There were bears everywhere. They were going to Switzerland.

"They're going to the Teddy Bears' Picnic," said Teddy. "They have one every year."

"Maybe we can go too," said Bunbury.
Kipper was not so sure.

"How can we?" he asked.

"Of course we can go," said Teddy. "This is a magic adventure."

Kipper and his friends went on the aeroplane to Switzerland. They flew over lakes and mountains.

"What a beautiful place for a picnic!" said Kipper.

When the plane landed everyone got off. There were lots and lots of bears. Kipper had never seen so many. They had come from all over the world. "It's going to be a big picnic," said Kipper.

There was a bus at the airport. It was going
to the Teddy Bears' Picnic.

"Come on," said Catsimir, "if we run we can
catch this bus."

Kipper liked Switzerland.

"It's beautiful here," said Kipper.

It was fun on top of the bus. The bears waved at everyone and everyone waved back.

At last the bus arrived. Everyone got off.
"I've never seen so many bears," said Kipper.
"We'd better stay together, in case we get lost."

Kipper and his friends found a good place to sit. Suddenly, everyone shouted and cheered. A famous bear had come on to the stage. He waved at the crowd.

"Welcome to the Teddy Bears' Picnic," he said.

"I know him," said Kipper. "He's a very famous bear indeed. I've read all his books."

Another famous bear came on to the stage.
He began to tell jokes and sing funny songs.
Everyone laughed and cheered.

"I know that famous bear, too," said Kipper.
"I've seen him on TV."

A famous pop group came on to the stage.
They played while the bears had their picnic.

"This is the best picnic I've ever been to,"
said Kipper.

Kipper had an autograph book. He wanted some of the famous bears to sign their names.

"I can show them to Biff and Chip," said Kipper. "Then they'll know I've had a magic adventure."

They went to find the famous bears. But there
was trouble. Some nasty bears were pushing the
famous bears into a car.

"It's a kidnap," said Bunbury. "We must do
something."

The car sped away. Catsimir saw a van.

"Come on!" he shouted. "Get in! We can follow the kidnappers in this van!"

Catsimir drove the van as fast as he could.
The car went even faster. It drove up a mountain
road.

"Faster, faster," called Bunbury.

"Don't lose them!" called Teddy.

The car drove through some big gates and stopped in front of a house. The famous bears were pushed inside.

"It looks dangerous," said Kipper, "but we must rescue them. I have a plan."

Kipper and Catsimir went to the house. Kipper rang a bell. Some nasty bears came to the door.

"Free honey!" called Kipper. "Free honey for every bear."

The nasty bears were greedy and they couldn't resist the honey. They didn't see what Teddy and Bunbury were doing. Teddy went to the car and took out the keys.

Bunbury went to the back of the house and
looked through a window. He saw the famous bears.
They were tied up.

Bunbury set the famous bears free. Then they all climbed out of the window.

"Come on," said Teddy. "Follow me and don't make a sound."

The famous bears crept into the honey van.
The nasty bears didn't see them because they
were too busy eating the honey.

One of the nasty bears saw that the famous bears were escaping.

"They're in the honey van!" he shouted. "Go after it!"

Catsimir drove the honey van as fast as he could. The nasty bears ran after the van but they got stuck in the honey.

"Hooray!" shouted Kipper.

The famous bears were pleased with Kipper and his friends.

"You were very clever," they said. "Thanks to you the Teddy Bears' Picnic can go on!"

The magic key began to glow. It was time for
Kipper's adventure to end.

"I can't wait to tell Biff and Chip about it,"
he said.

"The magic key glowed last night," said Kipper.
"I had a magic adventure."

"We don't believe you," said Biff.

"No, it was just a dream," said Chip.